FIRST TIME LEARNING

Numbers

Key skills for early learning
Prepares for starting school

3+ Preschool

Numbers

Here's a short note for parents:

We recommend that you work through this book with your child, offering guidance and encouragement along the way. Try to find a quiet place to sit, preferably at a table, and encourage your child to hold his or her pencil correctly. Try to work at your child's pace and avoid spending too long on any one page or activity. Most of all, emphasize the fun element of what you are doing and enjoy this special and exciting time!

Autumn
Publishing

Know your numbers!

How old are you?
Can you see that number on this page?

Count **1, 2, 3, 4, 5.** Then **5, 4, 3, 2, 1.**

Find the missing cake sticker.

Place your sticker here

Place your reward sticker here

Count the candles on each cake
and say the numbers.

1 2 3 4 5 6 7 8 9 10

Birthday candles

Count the candles and draw a circle around the number.

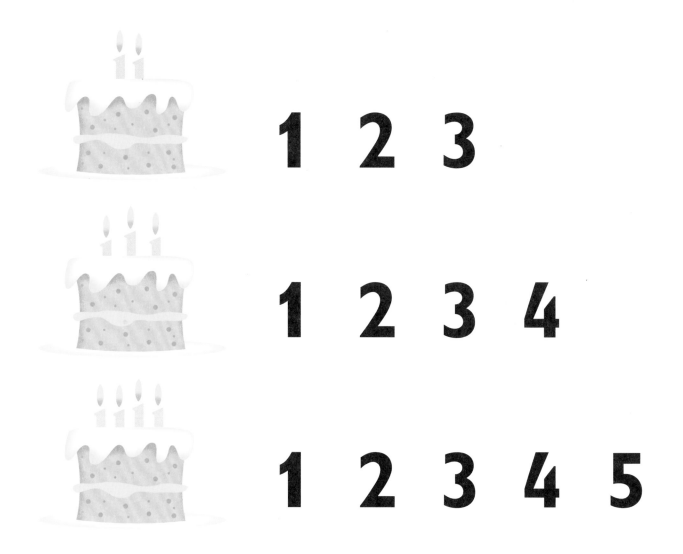

1 2 3

1 2 3 4

1 2 3 4 5

Birthday presents

Find a sticker of some presents.
Count the birthday presents.

Place your
sticker here

Place your
reward sticker
here

More numbers

Count **6, 7, 8, 9, 10**, then all the way back again – **10, 9, 8, 7, 6!**

Find a sticker with two ducks.

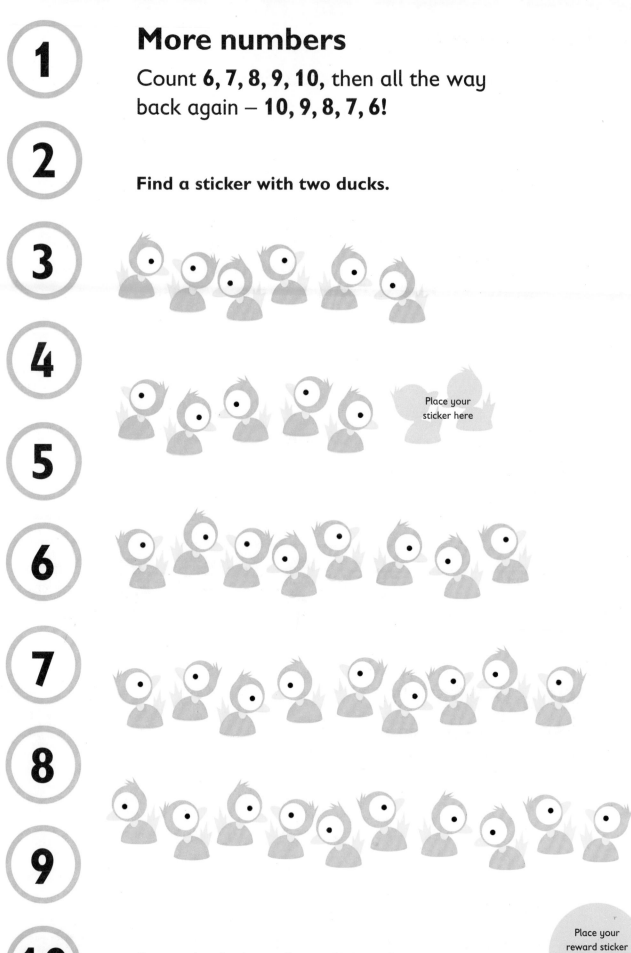

Place your sticker here

Count the ducks and say the numbers.

Place your reward sticker here

Quack, quack

Count the ducks and circle the number.

6 7 8 9 10

6 7 8 9 10

Frog march

Find a sticker with two frogs.
Count the frogs. Are there **7** frogs?

Place your
sticker here

Place your
reward sticker
here

Number rhymes

Here are two number rhymes to sing.

1, 2, 3, 4, 5 once I caught a fish alive

1, 2, 3, 4, 5 once I caught a fish alive,

6, 7, 8, 9, 10 then I let it go again.

Why did you let it go?

Because it bit my finger so.

Which finger did it bite?

This little finger on the right!

Place your sticker here

Place your reward sticker here

Find a fish sticker.
Count the fish in the picture and colour them in.

Sizzling sausages

Five fat sausages sizzling in a pan,

All of a sudden **one** went bang!

Four fat sausages sizzling in a pan,

All of a sudden **one** went bang!

Three fat sausages sizzling in a pan,

All of a sudden **one** went bang!

Two fat sausages sizzling in a pan,

All of a sudden **one** went bang!

One fat sausage sizzling in a pan,

All of a sudden **one** went bang!

Now there are no fat sausages sizzling in the pan!

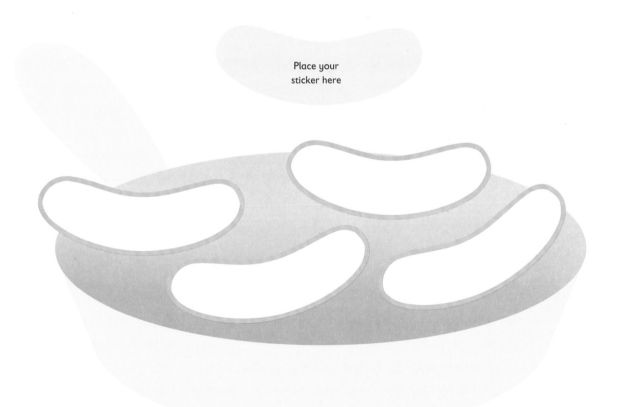

Place your
sticker here

Place your
reward sticker
here

Find a sausage sticker.
Count the sausages in the picture and colour them in.

Write 1, 2, 3, 4, 5

Numbers big and numbers small.
Can you count and write them all?

Count the dots. Say the numbers. Write the numbers.

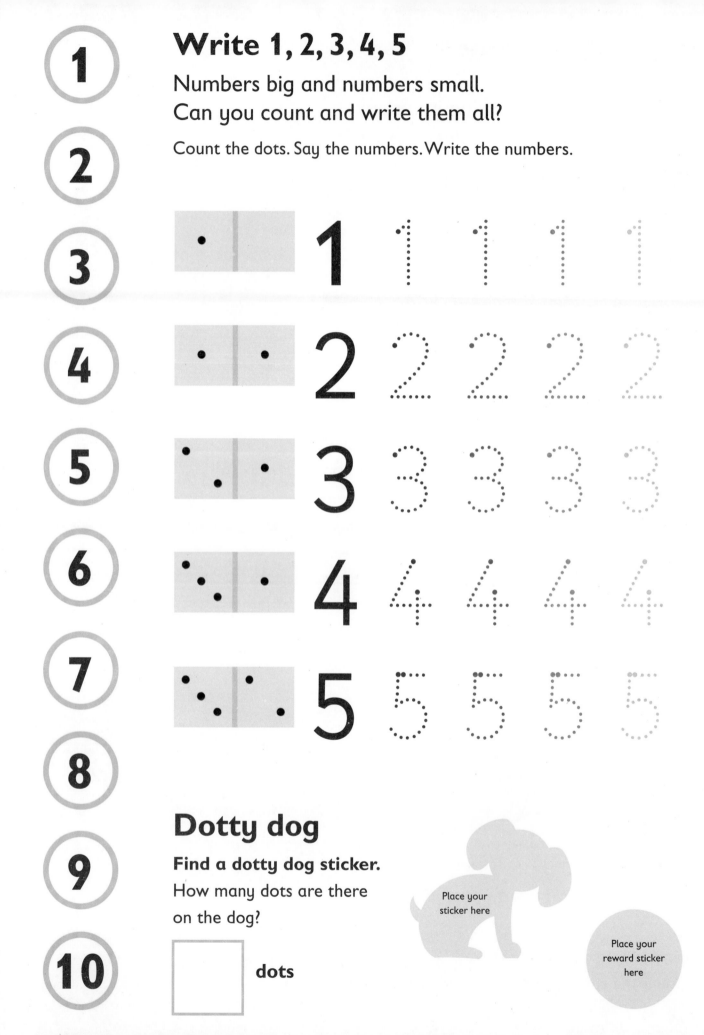

Dotty dog

Find a dotty dog sticker.
How many dots are there
on the dog?

Place your
sticker here

[ ] **dots**

Place your
reward sticker
here

Write 6, 7, 8, 9, 10

Count the dots. Say the numbers. Write the numbers.

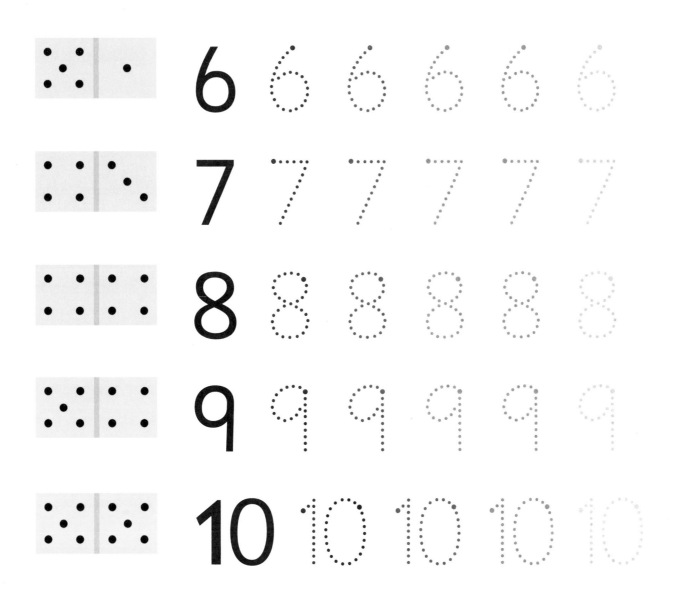

Spotty pig

Find a spotty pig sticker.

How many spots are there
on the pig?

spots

Place your
sticker here

Place your
reward sticker
here

Keep your toys tidy

Find the pencils sticker.
Now count all the toys.

Place your sticker here

How many are there? Write the numbers in the boxes.

balls **cars** **dinosaurs**

pencils **trains**

Place your reward sticker here

Paintbrushes and paint pots

Count the paintbrushes and write the numbers in the boxes.

Building blocks

Count the blocks. Draw lines to match the blocks with the numbered boxes.

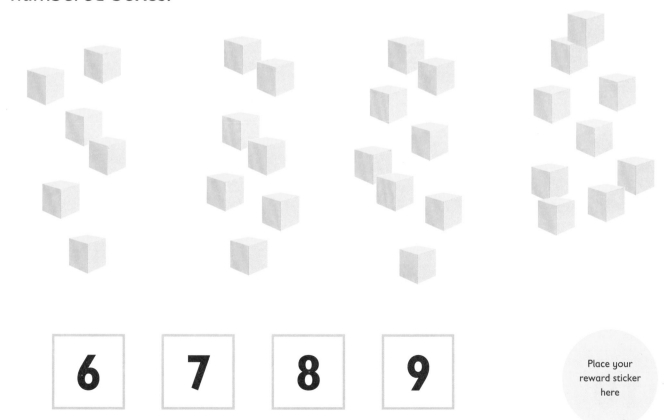

| 6 | 7 | 8 | 9 |

Colour the most

Colour the tree with the most birds.

Find a bird sticker.

Colour the bird with the most tail feathers.

Place your sticker here

Place your reward sticker here

What's missing?

Write the missing number on the egg in each line.

5 ⬭ 7 8 9 10

⬭ 6 7 8 9 10

5 6 7 ⬭ 9 10

Hoppity hop!

Count the hops the bird has made.

Find the number sticker.

(1) (2) (3) (4) (5) (Place your sticker here)

Count the hops and write the numbers.

(Place your reward sticker here)

One more

Draw one more thing in each line.

Then count the things in each line and write the number.

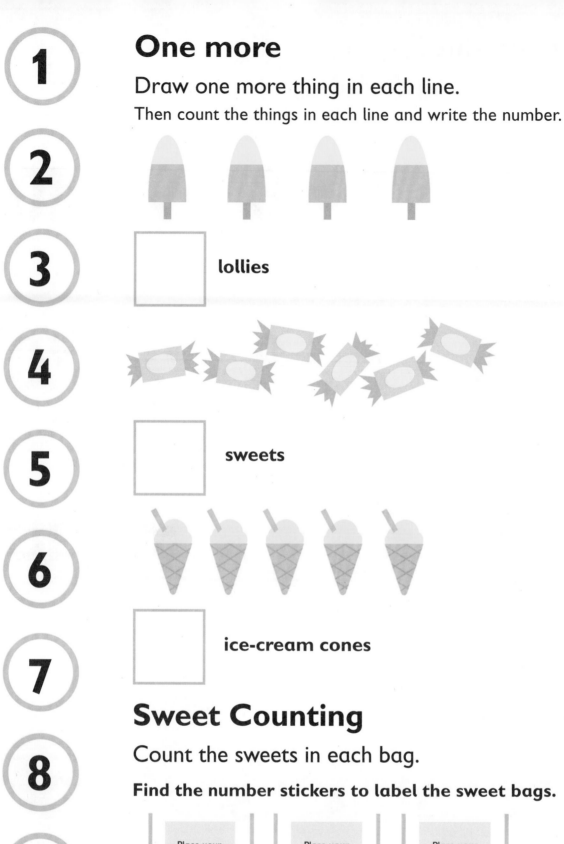

lollies

sweets

ice-cream cones

Sweet Counting

Count the sweets in each bag.

Find the number stickers to label the sweet bags.

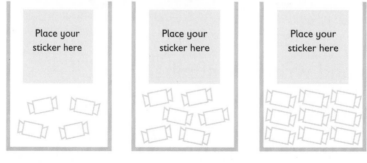

Place your sticker here

Place your sticker here

Place your sticker here

Place your reward sticker here

Colour the bag with the most sweets.

One less

Cross out one thing in each line and write the number of things left.

Cup Counting

Count the drinks on each tray and write the numbers in the boxes.

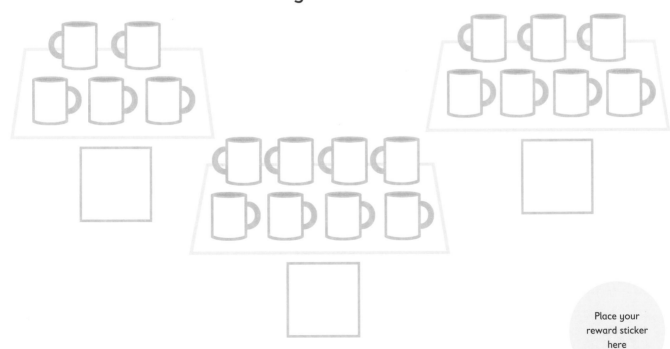

Colour the tray with the most drinks.

Counting fish

Find a sticker with two fish.
Count each school of fish. Say the numbers out loud.

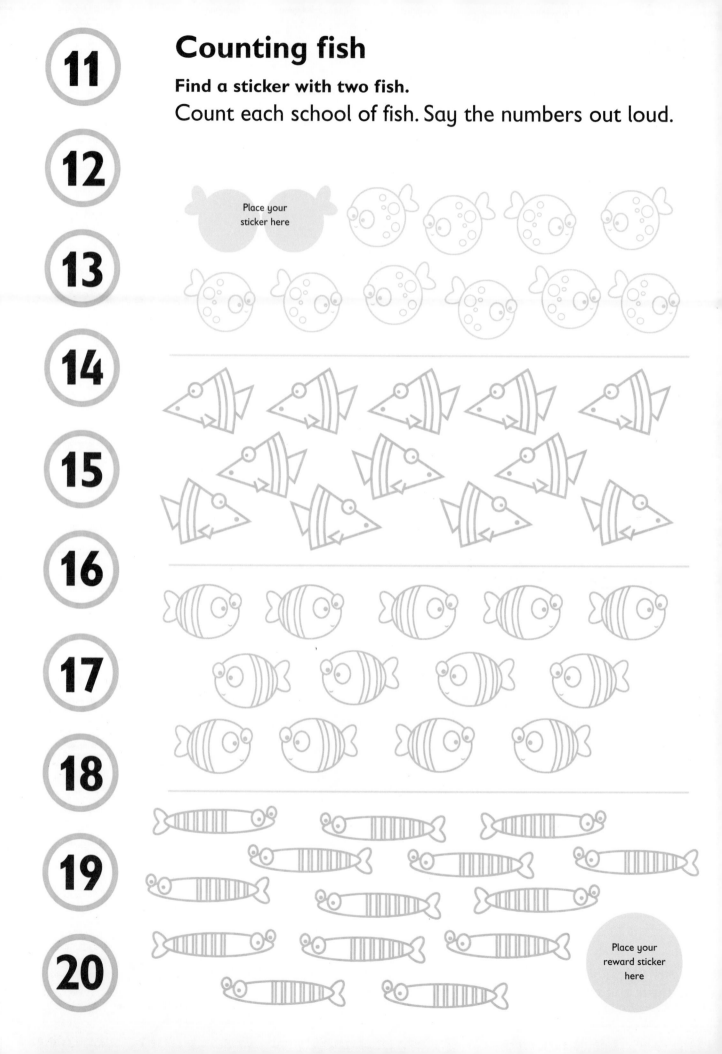

 Clever me!

 That's right!

 Well done!

 OK!

 Well done!

 I did it!

 Well done!

 That's right!

 Clever me!

 I did it!

 OK!

 Clever me!

 I did it!

 OK!

 Well done!

 I did it!

 That's right!

 OK!

 Well done!

 Clever me!

 Well done!

 OK!

 Clever me!

 I did it!

 That's right!

 OK!

 I did it!

 Well done!

 OK!

 Clever me!

 That's right!

 I did it!

 Clever me!

 Well done!

That's right!

Turtles

Count the turtles. Draw a circle around the number.

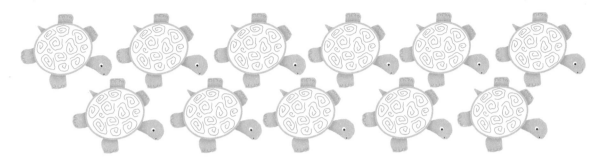

11 12 13 14 15

11 12 13 14 15

Starfish everywhere!

Count the starfish.

Place your
sticker here

Find a sticker with more starfish.

Now count how many starfish there are altogether.

Did you count **15** starfish?

Place your
reward sticker
here

Write 11, 12, 13, 14, 15

Find a domino sticker.

Count the dots. Trace the numbers with a pencil.

Flower show

Count the flowers. Write the numbers on the vases.

Seedlings to grow

Count each group of seeds. Draw lines to match the seeds to the packets.

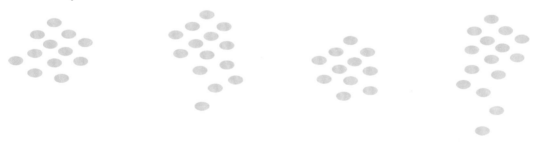

11

12

14

15

Place your reward sticker here

11
12
13
14
15
16
17
18
19
20

More or less?

Find a butterfly sticker.
Count the butterflies in each group.
Write the numbers in the boxes.

Place your
sticker here

Place your
reward sticker
here

Which group has **more** butterflies?
Which group has **fewer** butterflies?
How many butterflies are there altogether?

What's missing?

Write the missing number on the leaf in each line.

10   11      13   14

10   11   12   13

10      12   13   14

Hoppity hop!

Count the hops the frog has made.

Find the number sticker.

(1) (2) (3) (4) (5) (6) (7)

(8) (9) (10) (11) (12) Place your sticker here

Place your reward sticker here

Two by two

Find the missing sticker.

Draw lines to match each pair of animals.
How many animal pairs are there altogether?

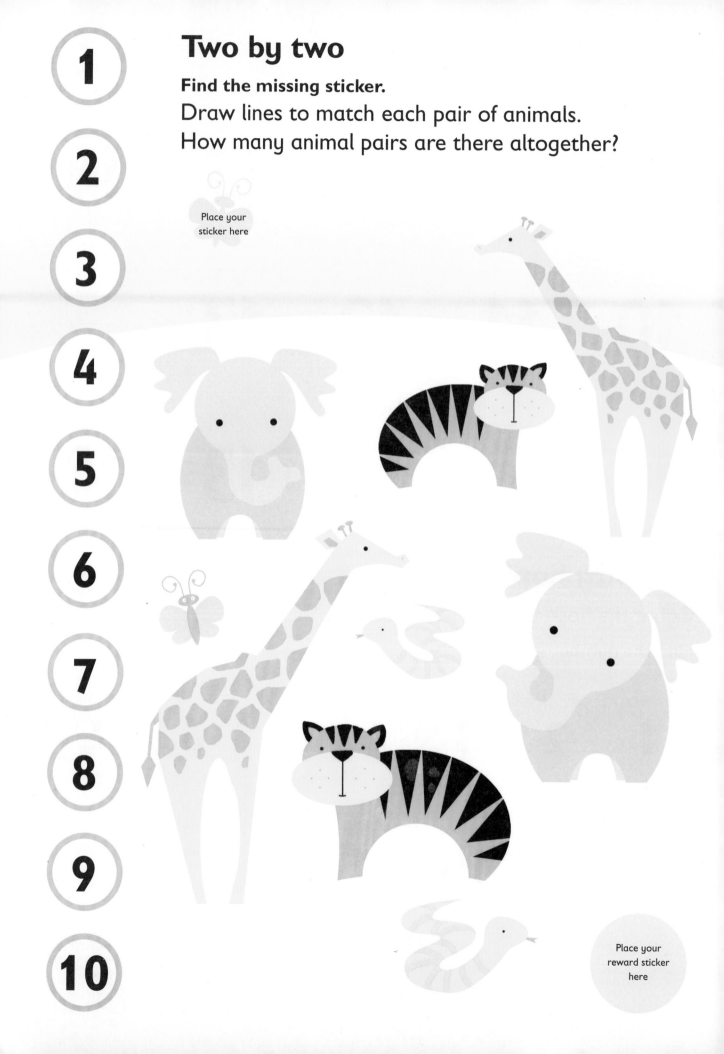

Place your sticker here

Place your reward sticker here

Two more

Draw **two** more things in each line. Count the cars and the cones.
Write the numbers in the boxes.

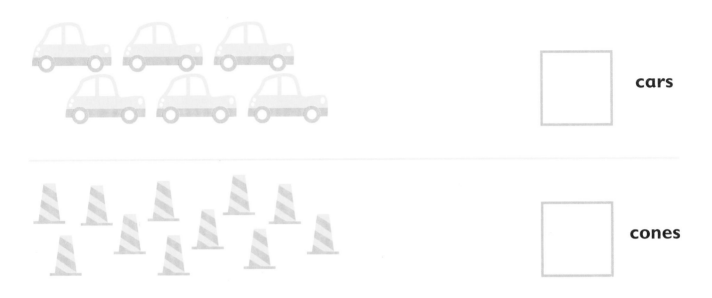

cars

cones

Two less

Cross out **two** things in each line. Count the things left in each line.
Write the number in the box.

socks

shoes

caps

Place your
reward sticker
here

Hide and seek numbers

Numbers here, numbers there, numbers hiding everywhere!

The numbers **1** to **15** are in this picture.

Can you find them all? Colour in the picture.

Place your
reward sticker
here

Numbers are everywhere!

Number **one**, number **two**,
is there a number on your shoe?

Number **three**, number **four**,
what's the number on your door?

Look around you. Can you see any numbers?
Write the numbers on the line.

....

What's your shoe size? ....

What's your house number? ....

**Find the missing number sticker
for the phone.**

Write your phone number here:

....

Place your
reward sticker
here

Tick tock! Tick tock!

Numbers tell us what time it is.

Find the missing number sticker for the clock.

What time is it?

Place your sticker here

Place your reward sticker here

11

12

13

14

15

16

17

18

19

20

Happy birthday to you!

Numbers tell you when it is your birthday.
Find the missing number sticker.
Find the day of your birthday on this calendar.
Colour in the square. How old are you now?
How old will you be on your next birthday?

1	2	3	4	5
6	7	8	9	10
11	12	13	14	15
16	17	18	Place your sticker here	20
21	22	23	24	25
26	27	28	29	30
31				

Place your reward sticker here

Don't forget!

Numbers help us to remember dates.

Write these date numbers.

Christmas day

....

My mum's birthday

....

My dad's birthday

....

Today's date

....

Best friend's birthday

....

Write some other important numbers here:

....

Now you won't forget them!

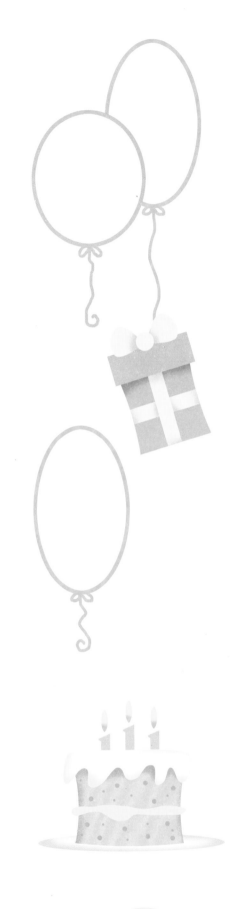

Place your reward sticker here

Big and small numbers

Numbers big and numbers small,
show me that you know them all!

What's the **smallest** number you know? ....

What's the **largest** number you know? ....

What's your favourite number? ....

Number machine

The crazy number machine has made some numbers.
Write the numbers in order in the circles.

Start with the **smallest** number.

5

16

15

2

10

20

Place your
reward sticker
here

Millions and billions!

These are huge, enormous, gigantic numbers.
They are bigger than you can count.

Just imagine the millions of stars that are in the sky!

Find a sticker with a huge, enormous, gigantic number.

Place your
sticker here

Place your
reward sticker
here

This is how we write **one million**.

Number dot-to-dot

Start at number **1** and join the numbered dots in order.

How many dots are there?

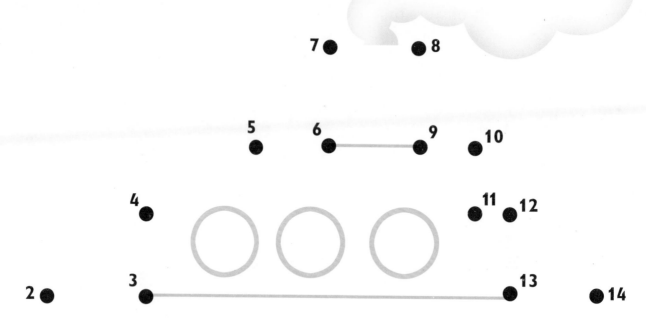

Well done! You're a star for finishing this book!

Place your reward sticker here